The Christmas Story

Stephanie Jeffs

Illustrated by Rhian Nest-James

Scripture Union

Introduction

This is the story of the first Christmas. It's the story of a baby called Jesus who was born 2,000 years ago in a far corner of the Roman Empire. His parents were poor, and being born in a stable was not a good start in life. Yet his birth, and what he did later, changed the history of the world.

For hundreds of years before Jesus was born, the Jewish people had cried out to God to rescue and save them. They believed that God had promised them a Saviour. The prophet Isaiah spoke of a child who would bring peace and justice into the world. The prophet Micah foretold that the little town of Bethlehem would be the birthplace of the Saviour. And so they waited for the Saviour to appear.

Jesus' birth took place at a time when many of God's people were longing to be set free from the Romans who occupied and ruled their land. But when he came, his message was of an even greater freedom and of a new relationship with God for everyone.

Two thousand years later, there are millions of followers of Jesus Christ all over the world.

The Angel's Visit

LUKE CHAPTER 1, VERSES 26–38

Mary was a happy young woman. She was engaged to be married to Joseph, the carpenter. She knew he would be a good husband for her.

One day, she was at work in her house in Nazareth when something happened that changed her life. The room was dark and cool, a sharp contrast from the brightness of the sun outside.

Suddenly there was light everywhere. Mary gasped and stumbled backwards and, as her eyes got used to the light, she saw someone standing in front of her.

'Mary,' said the angel, 'God is with you.'

At these words, Mary was terrified. She began to shake. The angel spoke again, 'I am Gabriel,' he said. 'Don't be afraid. God is pleased with you. You are going to have a baby, a son whom you will call Jesus. He will be God's Saviour for the world.'

Mary's mind raced, but she did not doubt that what the angel said was true.

'How can this happen?' she asked. 'I'm not even married yet.'

'God's Spirit will come over you. His power will rest on you, so that the baby will be called the Son of God.'

Mary sank to her knees. She felt quite calm. Her fear had gone. She looked up at Gabriel.

'I want to serve God,' she said. 'I will do whatever he wants.'

Mary and Elizabeth

LUKE CHAPTER 1, VERSES 39–56

After the angel had gone, Mary remembered that he had told her something else. 'Your cousin Elizabeth is going to have a baby!' he had said. 'So you see – nothing is impossible with God.'

Elizabeth and Zechariah had longed for a baby for many years, and now Elizabeth was past the age of child-bearing. So was it true what the angel had said? Mary knew, deep within her heart, that the angel was right. Nothing was impossible with God.

Mary left Nazareth and went to the hills where Elizabeth and Zechariah lived.

The house was quiet and still. Mary pushed open the door, and went to greet Elizabeth.

Elizabeth stood up, and as she did so, she cried out, clutching her stomach. She felt God's Spirit come over her and before Mary could tell any of her news, Elizabeth knew that Mary was to be the mother of God's special baby.

'You are blessed,' cried Elizabeth. 'You are to be the mother of the Saviour. Even my baby jumped for joy inside me when you arrived!'

Mary felt full of joy. The words tumbled from her mouth, 'Everything that is in me praises God,' she said. 'I am so happy that he is my Saviour!'

Mary and Elizabeth told each other everything that had happened. They praised God together.

Three months later, Mary returned home to Nazareth.

Joseph's Dream

MATTHEW CHAPTER 1, VERSES 18-25

Joseph sat in his carpenter's shop. He sighed and drew with his finger in the sawdust. 'I must do what is right for Mary,' he said to himself.

When he thought of Mary, he put his head in his hands. They had been engaged to be married for some time, and he had been so happy that she was to be his wife. She was young and full of life.

But then she had told him that she was pregnant, and things had changed. She kept trying to tell him other things which he did not understand. All he knew was that she was going to have a baby, and that he was not the father. They weren't even married! If the people of Nazareth found out, Mary would have a terrible time. There would be gossip.

Maybe the best thing to do would be to break off the engagement with as little fuss as possible. He still loved Mary. But he did not want to see her hurt.

Now that he had made up his mind, Joseph unrolled his mattress, lay down and fell asleep immediately. But as he slept, he dreamed. He saw an angel coming towards him. The angel spoke to him.

'Joseph!' said the angel. 'You must marry Mary. God is the father of the baby she is carrying. You must call him Jesus and he will be the Saviour!'

Joseph sat upright. Daylight streamed through the window. Suddenly he understood everything Mary had been trying to tell him.

'Mary will be my wife,' he said. He went to tell her about the dream. And after that they were soon married.

The Journey to Bethlehem

LUKE CHAPTER 2, VERSES 1–5

Emperor Augustus had ordered that a census should be taken of all the people in the Roman Empire. This was so that everyone could be made to pay taxes. Each family had to register in the town of their ancestors.

Joseph the carpenter was descended from the same family as King David, so he and Mary had to travel to Bethlehem in Judea. It was seventy miles away and the journey would take several days.

Joseph loaded up the donkey. Mary got ready. She knew that it was nearly time for her baby to be born. And so they left Nazareth in Galilee and set off.

It seemed as though the whole world was on the move. The roads were full of people, walking to their home towns.

Sometimes Mary walked with Joseph. Sometimes she rode on the donkey's back. They stopped for the night in small villages. They met and talked with other people making the same journey. At last they reached the small town of Bethlehem, the birthplace of King David.

The Baby in the Manger

Luke chapter 2, verses 6–7

By the time Mary and Joseph reached Bethlehem, the whole town was full of visitors.

'Where will we stay?' asked Mary wearily. She was tired and wanted to rest.

Joseph led the way through the narrow streets until he found an inn. He could tell it was full; there was so much noise coming from inside. He knocked.

'Yes?' said a woman, holding a jug in one hand and a loaf of bread in the other. 'What do you want?'

'Do you have a room we could stay in?' asked Joseph. 'My wife is expecting a baby.'

The woman looked at Mary. 'Go round the back,' she said. 'We're full up, but if you don't mind the animals, there's a place you can stay.'

While they were staying there, Mary gave birth to her baby. It was a boy, just as the angel had said. She wrapped him in some cloth that she had brought with her, and held him in her arms. Then, looking for somewhere for him to sleep, she saw the manger, full of hay, and put him gently in it.

Joseph looked at the tiny baby. 'His name is Jesus,' he said.

The Shepherds on the Hillside

Luke chapter 2, verses 8-15

A group of shepherds huddled together on the hillside outside Bethlehem. It was cold, and the red embers of the fire glowed in the darkness. They sat in silence. All was quiet, apart from the breathing of the sheep.

Suddenly, a sharp light ripped through the darkness and a voice spoke from the brightness.

'It's an angel!' gasped one of the shepherds. They clung to each other, shaking with fear.

'Don't be afraid!' said the angel. 'I have some good news which will bring great joy to the whole world! Tonight, in Bethlehem, a baby boy has been born. He is God's Saviour! See him for yourselves! You will find him, wrapped in strips of cloth, lying in a manger.'

Without warning, the whole sky burst into light and sound. Thousands of angels filled the sky. 'Glory to God in the highest,' they sang. 'Peace to his people on earth.'

They repeated the song over and over again until it echoed round the hills.

Slowly the light faded. Darkness returned.

'Let's see the baby for ourselves!' the shepherds cried, and ran down the hillside and into the silent streets of Bethlehem.

The Shepherds Find the Baby

LUKE CHAPTER 2, VERSES 16–19

The shepherds hurried to Bethlehem. They found the place where the baby was, and went in. They saw Mary and Joseph. Then they went to the manger and saw the tiny, new-born baby. What the angels had told them was true: God's Saviour had been born. They were full of wonder.

When the shepherds left the stable they told everyone what had happened that night. 'Praise God!' they said. 'A baby has been born. He is God's promised Saviour. Peace has come to earth!' Everyone who heard what the shepherds said were amazed.

Mary listened to all the special things being said about her baby. She thought about them over and over again, and wondered silently at what God had done.

'Praise God!' said Mary and Joseph, as they cradled the baby Jesus in their arms.

The shepherds returned to their sheep in the hills, singing praises to God for all that they had heard and seen.

The Message
of Simeon

LUKE CHAPTER 2, VERSES 21–35

Eight days later, Mary and Joseph took their baby to be circumcised. They knew what they were to call him. The angel had told them both. 'His name is Jesus,' they said.

A few weeks later, they left Bethlehem and travelled to Jerusalem to visit the temple. They went to make a sacrifice. They could not afford to sacrifice a lamb, so they bought a pair of doves.

An old man called Simeon lived in Jerusalem. He loved God, and he believed that he would not die before he had seen the Saviour God had promised to send to the world.

Suddenly, he heard God telling him to go to the temple. He made his way through the busy streets of Jerusalem, and walked towards the temple.

As soon as he saw the young woman holding her baby, he knew that the baby was God's Saviour. He held the baby in his arms, and stared into his face.

'Praise God!' he said. 'Now I can die in peace, because I have seen the Saviour of the world! This baby will be like a light, showing everyone the way to God.'

Carefully, Simeon handed the baby back to Mary. She looked at Joseph in amazement.

'May God bless you both,' Simeon said, and he left the temple.

The Message of Anna

LUKE CHAPTER 2, VERSES 36–40

There was also a very old woman called Anna who spent every day in the temple, praising and praying to God. She was eighty-four years old. For all of her life, she had been waiting for this moment. Like many people, she longed for the Saviour who would come to free God's people, and bring a new rule of peace to the earth.

As soon as Simeon had finished speaking to Joseph and Mary, Anna came up to them. When she saw the baby, she immediately gave thanks to God, for she knew at once that this was God's Saviour, who had come to save his people.

'Praise God!' she cried, 'for sending us this special baby.'

Then Anna went around the temple, telling everyone she met about the birth of Jesus.

Mary and Joseph left Jerusalem and returned with Jesus to Bethlehem.

The Wise Men from the East

MATTHEW CHAPTER 2, VERSE 1

Thousands of miles away, in an eastern land, there were some wise men who studied the stars. They were very interested in an exciting discovery – a bright new star. This star was full of meaning.

The wise men looked at charts and ancient documents, and they learned that the star they had seen was the sign that a new king had been born.

They decided to follow the star, and so they prepared for a great journey. They got together everything they would need: their horses, camels, servants, provisions, and gifts for a new king.

Their journey was long and hard, but always they followed the star. At last they reached Jerusalem, the capital of Judea.

They thought that the palace where King Herod lived was the place to find a new-born king. So they went to the palace, and asked to see the king.

The Wise Men meet King Herod

MATTHEW CHAPTER 2, VERSES 2-8

When it was announced that some wise men from the east had arrived at the palace gate, Herod was surprised. He was not expecting foreign visitors, but he agreed to see them.

'We are looking for the new king of the Jews that has been born,' said the wise men. 'We saw his star appear in the sky and have come to worship him.'

Herod was alarmed. He was afraid. He had heard nothing about a baby king. After all, he was the king.

He asked the wise men to wait and immediately called his advisors together.

'Tell me, do the Scriptures say where God's Saviour will be born?' he demanded.

'In Bethlehem,' they replied. 'It's all written in the book of Micah the prophet.'

Herod thought carefully. Then he called the wise men again. 'Look for the king in Bethlehem,' he said. 'If you find him, let me know as quickly as you can. I would like to worship him too.'

And so the wise men set off for Bethlehem, while Herod thought of ways to get rid of this 'baby king'.

The Wise Men
Worship the King

MATTHEW CHAPTER 2, VERSES 9-12

When the wise men left Herod's palace, they saw the star again. They were excited and happy. The star seemed to be guiding them, and so they followed it.

Before long, the star appeared to stop over a small house in Bethlehem.

They went inside and saw Mary with her little son, Jesus. They knew that this was the child they had been looking for.

The wise men knelt down before the baby king and gave him their gifts: finest gold, fit for a king; sweet frankincense and myrrh.

At last, they knew that their journey was over. They had found the king they had been looking for.

The wise men made ready to return to Jerusalem with the news. But the night before they left, God warned them in a strange dream: 'Don't go back to Jerusalem, and don't go back to Herod.'

The wise men set off towards the east on the long journey home, avoiding Jerusalem. As they went on their way, they praised God that they had seen the Saviour, the new King.

Published in the UK by Scripture Union
207-209 Queensway, Bletchley, Milton Keynes, Bucks MK2 2EB
ISBN 1 85999 303 6

First edition 1999

Printed and bound in Singapore